● Contents

CONTENTS

Introduction

How and when to assess

This Assessment Book provides teachers' notes and a photocopiable pupil assessment sheet for each unit (or group of units) of the programme. This structure gives complete flexibility to the teacher over how and when to assess.

You may decide to use the tests as a check-up for the whole class at the end of each unit.

You may decide, every few weeks, to photocopy the relevant sheets to make a 'mini-test' that can be administered either to the whole class, groups or targeted individuals.

The questions on the test are usually styled in a different way to the other practice materials in Abacus (i.e. Workbooks and Photocopy Masters). Your daily interaction with a child along with their work from the practice materials will always provide the first evidence of whether he or she has particular difficulties or strengths. The assessment sheets are designed to probe a child's deeper understanding, presenting them with unfamiliar contexts and styles of question. The aim of the Abacus approach is to produce children who are confident mathematicians, and who can tackle a variety of contexts and styles, building on what is familiar to them.

Within each teacher's section, the notes are organised under the following headings:

➤ **Skills assessed**, giving details of the exact mental and written skills covered in the unit. Key skills are the focus of the test.

➤ **Diagnostic materials**, detailing particular sections of the Workbook that directly practise the key skills identified above. These pages can be used in two ways:

- as a check of whether a particular child is ready for the test

- as further evidence of achievement.

➤ **Oral questions**, several questions that should be read out by the teacher at the start of the test. Answer boxes are provided on the assessment sheets. When administering the test, read each question twice, allowing about ten seconds between each reading. If you are using several different sheets as one test, you can either select a particular question from each sheet, or read out all the oral questions, with children recording their answers on a separate piece of paper.

➤ **Common difficulties**, giving advice on the kinds of common mistakes that children make, and how to remedy them.

➤ **Practice activities**, further practical activities focusing on the key skills, for children who need some further reinforcement.

➤ **Answers** to each test are also provided.

Each assessment sheet has a margin on the right, where you can record a child's score on each question. This can then be transferred to the foot of the page, and carried over, if appropriate, to the next sheet. Where children have answered incorrectly, but have shown some understanding or relevant working, you may decide to award half a mark.

Administering the tests

An introductory page for the children is provided on page 5, so that you can photocopy this each time a test is administered.

No calculators are required for any of the assessment sheets, and any other special equipment needed is specified in the Teachers' notes. The style of administration, e.g. formal, timed, or informal, untimed is entirely up to the individual teacher, and may be decided on a unit by unit basis. Each pupil assessment sheet will take between five and ten minutes.

Before starting, remind the children to read each question carefully. The assessment sheets are deliberately uncluttered and children can make use of any available space to work out the answer. 'Working' boxes are provided on the assessment sheets, where appropriate, for children to show their working, and are indicated by the following icon:

Tell the children, if they have difficulty with one of the questions, to move on to the next one – they can always return later. If they finish the test they should always go back and check their work (if you are timing the children, you may wish to build in some time for this).

National Curriculum Levels

The assessment sheets can be used in a variety of ways (either one sheet at a time, or grouped together), and for this reason it is difficult to allocate particular levels to child's test scores.

Clearly, it is impossible to assign a level from one test sheet in isolation, and no doubt different children will achieve at a higher or lower level on different topics during the year. If, every few weeks, a selection of sheets is administered as one test, then over the course of the year it will become clear whether particular children are consistently achieving at a high or low level.

On the whole, the assessment sheets test what it would be reasonable to assume the majority can achieve during Year 2 (P3) (i.e. solid level 2, working towards level 3, or level A working towards level B in Scotland).

Sensible decisions can therefore be made about children who regularly achieve very highly on the assessment sheets (e.g. consistently achieving 80-100% across a range of topics), those who fall into the 'middle' category (e.g. consistently in the band 60-80%) and those who have difficulties with a range of topics (e.g. consistently achieving less than 60%). You will need to make these judgements in conjunction with your everyday working knowledge of the particular child, and their strengths and weaknesses. You are in a unique position to decide if a test result is a 'one-off', or evidence of consistent achievement.

Instructions

- You do not need a calculator for any of the questions on these sheets.

- Work carefully through the questions.

- If you cannot do one of the questions, go on to the next one. You can come back to it later.

- When you have finished, go back and check your work.

- Read each question carefully before trying to answer.

- Use any space on the sheet to work out the answer.

- Some question have boxes like this. Show your working in these boxes, you may get a mark.

Numbers to 100

Skills summary

- To say the number names, in sequence, from zero to 100
- To say the number names, in sequence, from 100 to zero
- To count a set of objects up to 100
- To match a spoken number name to its written numeral (up to 100)
- To match a written numeral to its spoken number name (up to 100)
- To estimate a number of objects up to 50
- To recognise the relationship between tens and units

Diagnostic materials

Number Workbook 1, page 1
- Check children can write the numbers to 30, in order.

Number Workbook 1, page 4
- Check children recognise the tens and units in a 2-digit number.

Oral questions

Read each question twice. Allow about ten seconds after each reading.
1. Write 21.
2. Write the next number: 28, 29, 30, …
3. How many tens in this number (write '45' on the board)?
4. How many cubes? (Hold up three sticks of 10 and four loose cubes.)

Common difficulties

When counting, check that the children are able to bridge into new tens confidently. Check that they are saying the number names correctly – provide plenty of practice (counting in unison, or as individuals around the class). When reading and writing numbers, emphasise the patterns involved (some children may reverse the digits, e.g. writing 37 for 73). The number grid provides a useful visual aid for highlighting the patterns involved.
Discourage children from trying to give a precise answer when estimating (e.g. 32). Ask questions like: *Is it nearer 30 or 40?*

Practice activities

1 Take one or two handfuls of cubes and quickly estimate how many. Count the cubes to check (make sure you count them accurately – try grouping in twos).

2 Take a handful of 10p coins (up to ten) and a handful of 1p coins (up to 10). Estimate how much, then check by counting.

Answers			
1. 21	**2.** 31	**3.** 4	**4.** 34
5. 13	**6.** 39, 41	**7.** 30, 31	**8.** 88, 90
9. 6	**10.** 8	**11.** 32p	**12.** 55p

Name _____

1. [ ]   **2.** [ ]   **3.** [ ]   **4.** [ ]

[ ]/4

Write the missing numbers.

5. 12 [ ] 14

6.  [ ] 40 [ ]

7. 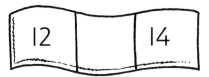 29 [ ] [ ]

8.  [ ] 89 [ ]

[ ]/4

Write how many tens.

9. 63 → [ ] tens   **10.** 81 → [ ] tens

[ ]/2

Write the totals.

11.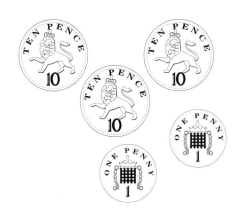

[ ] p

12.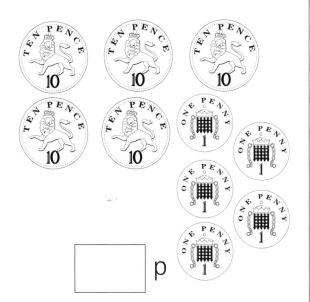

[ ] p

[ ]/2

Score: [ ]/12   Total: [ ]

Addition

Skills summary

- To know addition bonds to 10
- To begin to know addition bonds for numbers up to 10
- To add 10 to a 2-digit number
- To add a multiple of 10 to a 2-digit number
- To add 9 or 11 to a 2-digit number

Diagnostic materials

Number Workbook 1, page 7
- Check that the children know addition bonds to 10.

Number Workbook 1, page 16
- Check that the children know that only the tens change when they add 10.

Oral questions

Read each question twice. Allow about ten seconds after each reading.
1. I have four sweets, how many do I need to make ten? *6*
2. Three add what makes nine? *6.*
3. Write the total of 47 and 20. *67.*
4. What is 52 add 9? *61*

Common difficulties

Provide plenty of practice so that children have instant recall of addition bonds to 10. They can use their fingers to help.

Children should realise that when adding 10 (or multiples of 10) the value of the units does not change. If necessary, reinforce this in practical ways, e.g. using 10p and 1p coins, or base ten equipment, though the best mental image for adding ten is the number grid. It is important that children are confident adding ten, before using this as a shortcut for adding 9 or 11 – again the number grid provides the best image.

Practice activities

1 Shuffle a set of number cards (0 to 10). Deal them, one at a time, saying the addition bonds to 10 for each number. How quickly can you work through the set?

2 Throw a dice twice to create a 2-digit number. Add 10 and write the matching addition (use a number grid to help). Try adding 9, or 11.

Answers

1. 6	**2.** 6	**3.** 67	**4.** 61
5. 1	**6.** 2	**7.** 3	**8.** 2
9. (20, 0), (13, 7), (9, 11), (5, 15)		**10.** 6, 26, 36, 56, 66	
11. 15, 26, 37, 48			

Name _____

1. ☐   **2.** ☐   **3.** ☐   **4.** ☐

☐/4

Write the missing numbers.

5. $9 + \boxed{} = 10$ **6.** $6 + \boxed{} = 8$

7. $\boxed{} + 4 = 7$ **8.** $10 = \boxed{} + 8$

☐/4

9. Join the pairs that make 20.

☐/4

Complete the chains by adding.

10. $\boxed{6} \xrightarrow{+20} \bigcirc \xrightarrow{+10} \bigcirc \xrightarrow{+20} \bigcirc \xrightarrow{+10} \bigcirc$

11. $\boxed{4} \xrightarrow{+11} \bigcirc \xrightarrow{+11} \bigcirc \xrightarrow{+11} \bigcirc \xrightarrow{+11} \bigcirc$

☐/8

Score: ☐ /20   Total: ☐

Money

Skills summary

- To recognise coins (up to £2)
- To recognise relationships between coins
- To exchange a coin for the equivalent value of smaller coins
- To find total values of sets of mixed coins

Diagnostic materials

Number Workbook 1, page 9
- Check that the children can recognise coins of different values.

Number Workbook 1, page 10
- Check that the children can find totals of mixed coins.

Oral questions

Read each question twice. Allow about ten seconds after each reading.
1. Which two coins would you use to buy a 20p chocolate bar?   10p
2. How many 5p coins would you need to buy a 20p chocolate bar?   4
3. What is the total of 10p, 5p and 1p?   16p.
4. What is the total of 20p, 10p and 2p?   32p.

Common difficulties

Children need to be confident at coin recognition before attempting exchange. For children having difficulty focus first on smaller value coins (up to 20p).
Finding totals of mixed coins may cause some children difficulties – start with coins of all the same value, then extend to mixed sets, emphasising that each coin needs to be dealt with in turn, with children checking its value.

Practice activities

1 Write a list of amounts up to 20p. For each amount write the fewest coins you need to match. Which amounts need two coins? Which need three coins? Do any need four coins?

2 Using only silver coins, how many ways can you make £1? Which way uses the fewest coins? Which way uses the most?

Answers

1. 10p, 10p   **2.** 4   **3.** 16p   **4.** 32p
5. 20p, 10p, 5p   **6.** 20p, 20p, 10p, 5p, 1p
7. 36p   **8.** 18p
9. (10p, 10p → 20p), (2p, 2p, 1p → 5p), (5p, 5p → 10p)

Name _____

| 1. | | 2. | | 3. | | 4. | |

$\dfrac{\boxed{}}{4}$

Circle the fewest coins you need.

5.

6.

$\dfrac{\boxed{}}{4}$

Write how much

7.

 $\boxed{}$ p

8. $\boxed{}$ p

$\dfrac{\boxed{}}{4}$

9. Join matching amounts

$\dfrac{\boxed{}}{3}$

Score: $\boxed{}$ /15   Total: $\boxed{}$

Subtraction

Skills summary

- To understand subtraction as taking away from a number of objects
- To subtract from a number (up to 10)
- To subtract from a number (up to 20) not crossing 10

Diagnostic materials

Number Workbook 1, page 11
- Check that the children understand subtraction as taking away.

Oral questions

Read each question twice. Allow about ten seconds after each reading.
1. I have eight sweets and eat four. How many left? 4
2. I have 10p and spend 7p. How much change? 3.
3. What is fifteen take away three? 12
4. What is twenty take away four? 16

Common difficulties

When counting back in unison check that the spoken words are said clearly. Counting back can be more difficult than counting forwards, and children will need lots of oral practice work (particularly for the 'teen' numbers).
Reinforce subtractions using the number line – children may like to make their own. Point to the first number in the subtraction, count back to match the second. Where do you land?

Practice activities

1 Take a handful of 1p coins (between 6 and 10). Throw a dice and take away that many. Write a matching subtraction.

2 Select a number card at random from a set (15 to 20). Count back four. Use a number line to help.

Answers

1. 4	**2.** 3p	**3.** 12	**4.** 16
5. 2	**6.** 3	**7.** 4	**8.** 7
9. 12	**10.** 12	**11.** 13	**12.** 14
13. 20, 17, 15, 12		**14.** 18, 16, 14, 11	

Name _____

1. [ ]   **2.** [ ]   **3.** [ ]   **4.** [ ]

$\dfrac{\square}{4}$

Write the missing numbers.

5. $10 - 8 = \boxed{}$ **6.** $9 - 6 = \boxed{}$

7. $8 - \boxed{} = 4$ **8.** $\boxed{} - 5 = 2$

$\dfrac{\square}{4}$

Complete these by counting back.

9. $18 \xrightarrow{\text{count back } 6} \boxed{}$ **10.** $15 \xrightarrow{\text{count back } 3} \boxed{}$

11. $17 \xrightarrow{\text{count back } 4} \boxed{}$ **12.** $16 \xrightarrow{\text{count back } 2} \boxed{}$

$\dfrac{\square}{4}$

Complete the chains by taking away.

13.

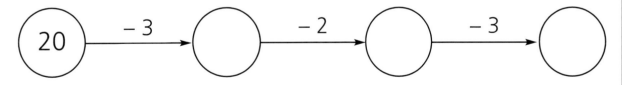

14.

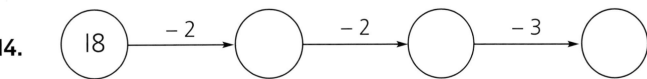

$\dfrac{\square}{6}$

Score: [ ] /18   Total: [ ]

Numbers to 100

Skills summary

- To count in ones and twos from zero to 100
- To count in ones and twos from 100 to zero
- To recognise odd and even numbers
- To recognise patterns in addition
- To compare two 2-digit numbers recognising the larger and smaller
- To recognise the number that lies between two 2-digit numbers
- To write three 2-digit numbers in order

Diagnostic materials

Number Workbook 1, page 19
- Check that the children can recognise odd and even numbers.

Number Workbook 1, page 23
- Check that the children can recognise numbers that come between two given numbers.

Oral questions

Read each question twice. Allow about ten seconds after each reading.
1. Write down the smallest number of these: 16, 14, 19.   *14*
2. Write down the largest number of these: 25, 15, 35.   *35*
3. Is 18 odd or even? Write 'o' for odd and 'e' for even.   *e*
4. Is 23 odd or even?   *o*

Common difficulties

Some children may find it difficult to recognise even numbers in the thirties, fifties, seventies and nineties because the first digit is odd (and similarly for odd numbers in the twenties, forties, ...). Emphasise that the even or odd pattern applies only to the units digit of the number.

For children who have difficulty ordering 2-digit numbers, emphasise the importance of the tens (match numbers with 10p and 1p coins, or base ten equipment before ordering). Numbers with more tens are larger.

Practice activities

1 Deal ten cards at random from a set (0 to 100). Quickly sort them into two piles: odd and even. Repeat.

2 Deal five cards at random from a set (0 to 20). Arrange them in order from smallest to largest. Repeat, perhaps extending to cards (0 to 50) or (0 to 100).

Answers

1. 14	**2.** 35	**3.** e	**4.** o
5. 12, 14, 16	**6.** 11, 13, 15	**7.** 34, 32, 30	**8.** 14
9. 30	**10.** 39	**11.** 60	**12.** 14, 18, 22
13. 16, 24, 35, 42			

Name _____

1. [   ]   **2.** [   ]   **3.** [   ]   **4.** [   ]

$\dfrac{\square}{4}$

Write the missing numbers.

5. 6,   8,   10,   [   ] ,   [   ] ,   [   ]

6. 5,   7,   9,   [   ] ,   [   ] ,   [   ]

7. 40,   38,   36,   [   ] ,   [   ] ,   [   ]

$\dfrac{\square}{3}$

Write the 'between' numbers.

8. | 13 | | 15 |

9. | 29 | | 31 |

10. | 38 | | 40 |

11. | 59 | | 61 |

$\dfrac{\square}{4}$

Write each list in order, from smallest to largest.

12. 18, 22, 14   _____

13. 35, 42, 16, 24   _____

$\dfrac{\square}{2}$

Score: [   ] /13   Total: [   ]

Addition and money

Skills summary

- To understand that two numbers can be added in any order
- To add two 1-digit numbers by counting on from the larger
- To select coins to make amounts (up to 50p)
- To select the fewest coins to pay for amounts (up to 50p)

Diagnostic materials

Number Workbook 1, page 28
- Check that the children can use appropriate strategies to add two 1-digit numbers.

Oral questions

Read each question twice. Allow about ten seconds after each reading.
1. What is ten add five?
2. What is the total of ten and seven?
3. Nine and four more makes...?
4. What should be added to eight to make thirteen?

Common difficulties

Using a 'counting on' strategy, emphasise that it is most efficient to start with the largest number first. Demonstrate, using cubes if necessary, that the order of addition makes no difference to the answer. For children who have difficulty with counting on, use the number line as reinforcement.

Rehearse addition bonds to ten regularly and use these as a strategy in completing additions. Use practical apparatus (e.g. 1p and 10p coins, interlocking cubes) to demonstrate how one number can be made up to 10 first, before counting on the remainder.

When finding the fewest coins to make amounts, children should be encouraged to be systematic, always starting with the largest value coins first.

Practice activities

1 Deal two cards at random from a set (5 to 9). Match each with a tower of cubes. Make one tower up to 10, with cubes from the other tower. Complete the addition by counting on.

2 Deal a card at random from a set (1 to 30). Find the fewest coins you need to match it. Repeat for ten cards.

Answers			
1. 15	**2.** 17	**3.** 13	**4.** 5
5. 4	**6.** 4	**7.** 6	**8.** 8
9. 13	**10.** 13	**11.** 12	**12.** 9
13. 20p, 10p, 10p, 2p, 1p		**14.** 20p, 10p, 5p	

Name _____

1. [ ]   **2.** [ ]   **3.** [ ]   **4.** [ ]

□/4

Write the missing numbers.

5. 6 + [ ] = 10   **6.** 8 + [ ] = 12

7. [ ] + 5 = 11   **8.** 14 = [ ] + 6

□/4

Complete these by counting on.

9. 8 $\xrightarrow{\text{count on 5}}$ [ ]   **10.** 7 $\xrightarrow{\text{count on 6}}$ [ ]

11. 9 $\xrightarrow{\text{count on 3}}$ [ ]   **12.** 6 $\xrightarrow{\text{count on 3}}$ [ ]

□/4

Circle the fewest coins you need.

13. 43p

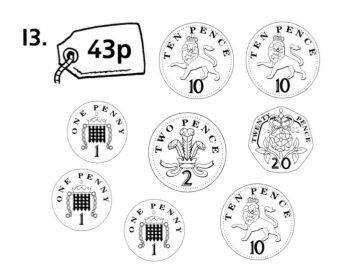

14. 35p

□/4

Score: [ ] /16   Total: [ ]

Twos and tens

Skills summary

- To count in twos from zero
- To begin to recognise sets of two
- To count in tens from zero
- To understand and use the '×' sign
- To learn ×2 multiplication facts
- To learn ×10 multiplication facts

Diagnostic materials

Number Workbook 1, page 32

- Check that the children can count in twos, and understand the multiplication sign.

Oral questions

Read each question twice. Allow about ten seconds after each reading.

1. What are three twos?   6
2. What is the next number: eight, ten, twelve, ...?   14
3. What is two times ten?   20
4. What are six tens?   60

Common difficulties

Most children enjoy the chanting aspects of counting in twos or tens, and you should practice this regularly.

It is important to ensure the children have plenty of experience of grouping objects in twos (use the children themselves, e.g. how many legs, ears, eyes, hands).

Some children may confuse the '×' sign with the '+' sign. Reinforce its meaning by reading it as 'lots of' or 'sets of' (e.g. three lots of ten).

Practice activities

1 Shuffle a set of number cards (1 to 10). Deal them, one at a time, saying that number of twos. How quickly can you work through the set? Repeat for tens.

2 Take a handful of 10p coins (up to ten). Count them in tens and write a matching multiplication. (Variation: use 2p coins.)

Answers

1. 6	**2.** 14	**3.** 20	**4.** 60
5. 8, 10, 12, 14		**6.** 14, 16, 18, 20, 22	
7. 4	**8.** 5	**9.** 7	**10.** 6
11. 50	**12.** 6	**13.** 90	**14.** 4

Name _____

1. ☐ **2.** ☐ **3.** ☐ **4.** ☐

☐/4

Complete the chains by adding 2.

5.

6.

☐/2

Write how many 2p coins you need to match each amount.

7. 8p ☐ 2p coins **8.** 10p ☐ 2p coins

9. 14p ☐ 2p coins **10.** 12p ☐ 2p coins

☐/4

Write the missing numbers.

11. 5 lots of 10 = ☐ **12.** ☐ lots of 10 = 60

13. 9 lots of 10 = ☐ **14.** ☐ lots of 10 = 40

☐/4

Score: ☐ /14   Total: ☐

Fractions

Skills summary

• To recognise one half of a shape
• To recognise one quarter of a shape

Diagnostic materials

Number Workbook 1, page 38
• Check children can recognise a half of a shape.

Oral questions

Draw four different shapes on the board, with halves and quarters shaded.
Point to each shape in turn, asking whether a half or a quarter is shaded.

Common difficulties

It is important that children understand that the two halves (or four quarters)
should all be the same size. Reinforce by folding different shapes.

Practice activities

1 Draw a series of 2 × 2 squares on squared paper. How many different ways are there of dividing each one in half?

2 Draw a series of 2 × 2 squares on squared paper. How many different ways are there of dividing each one into quarters?

Answers

1–4. Answers will vary.
   5. half   **6.** quarter   **7.** quarter   **8.** half
9–12. Answers will vary.

Name _____

I. [box] **2.** [box] **3.** [box] **4.** [box]

$\frac{\square}{4}$

Write what fraction of each shape is shaded.

5.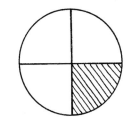

_____

6.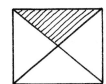

_____

7.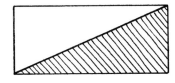

_____

8.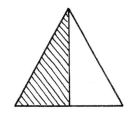

_____

$\frac{\square}{4}$

Colour matching fractions of each shape.

q. 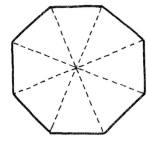 half [rectangle]

10.  quarter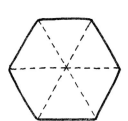

II.  quarter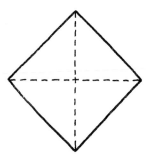

12.  half [hexagon]

$\frac{\square}{4}$

Score: [____] /12   Total: [____]

Numbers to 100

Skills summary

- To count on and back in multiples of 10
- To count on in tens from a 2-digit number
- To count back in tens from a 2-digit number
- To understand the value of each digit in a 2-digit number
- To partition a 2-digit number into tens and units

Diagnostic materials

Number Workbook 2, page 1
- Check that the children can add 10 to a 2-digit number.

Number Workbook 2, page 5
- Check that the children understand the value of each digit in its place in a 2-digit number.

Oral questions

Read each question twice. Allow about ten seconds after each reading.
1. What is 16 add 10?
2. Ten more than seventy three is...?
3. What is 27 count back 10?
4. Ten less than 48 is...?

Common difficulties

Children may have difficulty partitioning a 2-digit number into tens and units. Emphasise the structure of the number using coins, or base-ten equipment. Match the spoken number name (e.g. forty-five), and the visual image (e.g. four 10p coins and five 1p coins) to the written number (i.e. 45).

Demonstrate that when adding 10 (or subtracting 10) only the tens digit changes.

Practice activities

1 Deal a card at random from a set (1 to 100). Match it with 10p and 1p coins. Say aloud, for example, forty-six is four tens and six units.

2 Deal a card at random from a set (1 to 100). Find the numbers 10 more and 10 less, if possible. Write the three numbers in order. Repeat.

Answers

1. 26	**2.** 83	**3.** 17	**4.** 38
5. 14	**6.** 58	**7.** 71	**8.** 9
9. 1, 11, 21, 31, 41, 51, 61		**10.** 64, 54, 44, 34, 24, 14, 4	

11. 63 → six tens
45 → four tens
54 → four units
16 → six units

Name _____

1. [ ]   **2.** [ ]   **3.** [ ]   **4.** [ ]

$\dfrac{}{4}$

Complete these.

5. 4 $\xrightarrow{\text{add 10}}$ [ ]   **6.** 48 $\xrightarrow{\text{add 10}}$ [ ]

7. 81 $\xrightarrow{\text{take away 10}}$ [ ]   **8.** 19 $\xrightarrow{\text{take away 10}}$ [ ]

$\dfrac{}{4}$

---

9. Complete the chain by adding 10.

10. Complete the chain by taking away 10.

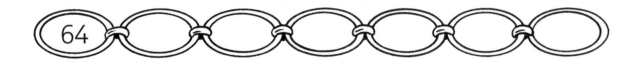

$\dfrac{}{4}$

---

11. Join each number to the correct label.

 63   45

54    16

six tens

four tens

four units

six units

$\dfrac{}{4}$

Score: [ ] /16   Total: [ ]

Addition

Skills summary

- To find the double of a number (up to 10) by adding
- To add two 1-digit numbers, using known doubles
- To double multiples of 10 (up to 100)
- To know addition bonds to 10
- To know addition bonds for numbers up to 10

Diagnostic materials

Number Workbook 2, page 8
- Check that the children are able to double the numbers up to 10.

Number Workbook 2, page 9
- Check that the children can use their knowledge of doubles, to add near doubles.

Oral questions

Read each question twice. Allow about ten seconds after each reading.
1. What is seven add seven?
2. What is double four?
3. What is the total of eight and nine?
4. What goes with eight to make ten?

Common difficulties

Doubles of numbers which cross ten are more difficult (focus first on doubles of numbers up to 5). Encourage children to read additions carefully, looking for near-doubles (i.e. numbers that are 'next to each other').

Practice activities

1 Shuffle a set of number cards (1 to 10). Deal them, one at a time, saying the double of each. How quickly can you work through the set?

2 Place a set of number cards (1 to 10) in order, in a line. Choose two 'next door' numbers and add them. Repeat.

Answers			
1. 14	**2.** 8	**3.** 17	**4.** 2
5–8. Answers will vary.			
9. 11	**10.** 17	**11.** 15	**12.** 13
13. 4	**14.** 7	**15.** 4	**16.** 2

Name _____

1. [ ]   2. [ ]   3. [ ]   4. [ ]

$\frac{\boxed{}}{4}$

Write pairs of numbers for each total.

5. $\boxed{} + \boxed{} = 10$ 6. $\boxed{} + \boxed{} = 12$

7. $\boxed{} + \boxed{} = 6$ 8. $\boxed{} + \boxed{} = 12$

$\frac{\boxed{}}{4}$

Complete these.

9. $5 + 6 = \boxed{}$ 10. $8 + 9 = \boxed{}$

11. $7 + 8 = \boxed{}$ 12. $6 + 7 = \boxed{}$

$\frac{\boxed{}}{4}$

Write the missing numbers.

13. $\boxed{} + 4 = 8$ 14. $10 = \boxed{} + 3$

15. $9 = 5 + \boxed{}$ 16. $7 + \boxed{} = 9$

$\frac{\boxed{}}{4}$

Score: [ ] /16   Total: [ ]

Subtraction

Skills summary

- To subtract 10 from a 2-digit number
- To subtract a multiple of 10 from a 2-digit number
- To subtract 9 or 11 from a 2-digit number

Diagnostic materials

Number Workbook 2, page 13
- Check that the children can subtract 10 from a 2-digit number.

Oral questions

1. What is 23 take away 10?
2. What is 48 count back 10?
3. What is ten less than 59?
4. What is 23 take away 11?

Common difficulties

When subtracting 10, use a number grid as a visual aid, and provide plenty of practice counting forwards and backwards in tens. Make sure the children are not counting back in ones.

When subtracting 9 or 11 ensure the children subtract 10 first, before making any adjustments (again the number grid is a useful visual aid).

Practice activities

1 Deal a number card at random from a set (1 to 100). Take away 10 and write the matching subtraction. Use 10p and 1p coins to help.

2 Deal a number card at random from a set (1 to 100). Take away 11 and write the matching subtraction. Use a number grid to help.

Answers

1. 13	**2.** 38	**3.** 49	**4.** 12

5. 54 – 20 = 34, 42 – 10 = 32, 38 – 30 = 8, 28 – 10 = 18

6. 94, 84, 64, 54		**7.** 78, 67, 56, 45	
8. 19	**9.** 31	**10.** 39	**11.** 27

Name _____

1. [ ]   **2.** [ ]   **3.** [ ]   **4.** [ ]

$$\frac{\boxed{}}{4}$$

5. Join each subtraction to the correct answer.

Complete each chain by subtracting.

6. (94) — 10 → ( ) — 20 → ( ) — 10 → ( )

7. (78) — 11 → ( ) — 11 → ( ) — 11 → ( )

$$\frac{\boxed{}}{2}$$

Complete these.

8. 30 − 11 = [ ]   **9.** 42 − 11 = [ ]

10. 48 − 9 = [ ]   **11.** 36 − 9 = [ ]

$$\frac{\boxed{}}{4}$$

Score: [ ] /14   Total: [ ]

Numbers to 100

Skills summary

- To count in steps of 5 from zero (up to 30)
- To count back in steps of 5 to zero, from an appropriate 2-digit number
- To count on and back in steps of 3

Diagnostic materials

Number Workbook 2, page 17
- Check that the children can count in steps of different size.

Oral questions

Read each question twice. Allow about ten seconds after each reading.
1. What is the next number: zero, five, ten, ...?
2. What number is missing: two, four, eight, ten?
3. What is three more than 15?
4. What is three less than 12?

Common difficulties

The number grid (1 to 100) is the best visual aid for counting in fives – the pattern is very clear. The oral count in fives also has a repetitive aspect which children will enjoy.
Counting in threes may be more difficult, but an aid such as a number grid or number line can be helpful.

Practice activities

1 On squared paper draw a grid with five columns and ten rows. Write the numbers 1 to 30 in the grid and colour the fives.

2 Use number cards (1 to 30). Place them in rows of three, in order: 1, 2, 3, then 4, 5, 6 underneath, then 7, 8, 9, ... Count the threes aloud.

Answers

1. 15	**2.** 6	**3.** 18	**4.** 9
5. 15, 20, 25, 35		**6.** 50, 45, 40, 35, 30	
7. 18, 21, 24, 27		**8.** 35, 10, 15, 30	
9. 15	**10.** 21	**11.** 21	**12.** 24

Name _____

1.   **2.**   **3.**   **4.** [ ]

$\frac{\Box}{4}$

Write the missing numbers.

5.

| 5 | 10 | | | | 30 | |

6.

| 60 | 55 | | | | |

7.

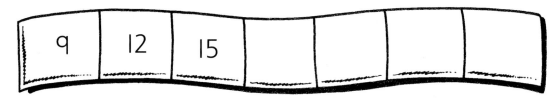

| 9 | 12 | 15 | | | | |

$\frac{\Box}{3}$

8. Circle the fives.

35   18   10   53   15   30   12

$\frac{\Box}{4}$

Complete these.

9. 12 $\xrightarrow{\text{add 3}}$ [ ]   **10.** 18 $\xrightarrow{\text{add 3}}$ [ ]

11. 24 $\xrightarrow{\text{take away 3}}$ [ ]   **12.** 27 $\xrightarrow{\text{take away 3}}$ [ ]

$\frac{\Box}{4}$

Score: [ ] /15   Total: [ ]

Addition and subtraction

Skills summary

- To choose the appropriate operation (addition or subtraction) in the context of a problem
- To add or subtract a 1-digit number to or from a 'teens' number
- To use knowledge of number facts to partition when adding or subtracting
- To recognise the number one more or less than a 2-digit number
- To recognise the number ten more or less than a 2-digit number

Diagnostic materials

Number Workbook 2, page 20
- Check that the children can interpret problems correctly.

Number Workbook 2, page 24
- Check that the children can recognise 10 more or less than a 2-digit number.

Oral questions

Read each question twice. Allow about ten seconds after each reading.

1. I have twelve oranges and five bananas. How many more oranges do I have?

2. The difference between 34 and 40 is ...?

3. What is ten add 4 add 3?

4. Ten add 5 take away 3 is ...?

Common difficulties

Ensure children read and understand the whole problem, before attempting a solution. They should look out for words such as 'total' or 'altogether' which imply addition, or 'less' or 'difference' which imply subtraction.

Emphasise, on the number grid, that adding one moves us one place to the right, adding ten moves us one place down.

Practice activities

1 Take a handful of coins (10p and 1p). Think of a problem using this amount – try it out on a partner. Write an addition or subtraction to match.

2 Deal a number card at random from a set (12 to 89). Imagine this is the middle square in a 3 × 3 section of a number grid. Write the 8 numbers that surround it.

Answers

1. 7	**2.** 6	**3.** 17	**4.** 12
5. 7p	**6.** 7p	**7.** 5p	**8.** 9p
9. 14, 15, 25, 26		**10.** 73, 63, 62, 52	

Name _____

1. [ ]   **2.** [ ]   **3.** [ ]   **4.** [ ]

$\frac{\ }{4}$

5. Renu bought a pencil and a rubber with 30p. Write how much change she will get.

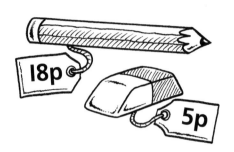

[ ] p

$\frac{\ }{3}$

Write how much more to make 15p.

6.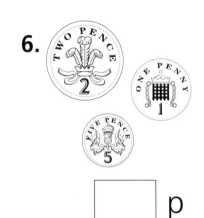

[ ] p

7.

[ ] p

8.

[ ] p

$\frac{\ }{3}$

Complete each chain.

9. (14) —+1→ ( ) —+10→ ( ) —+1→ ( )

10. (73) —−10→ ( ) —−1→ ( ) —−10→ ( )

$\frac{\ }{2}$

Score: [ ] /12   Total: [ ]

Addition and subtraction

Skills summary

- To add or subtract a 1-digit number to or from a 'teens' number
- To add or subtract a 1-digit number to or from a 'twenties' number
- To use knowledge of number facts to partition when adding or subtracting

Diagnostic materials

Number Workbook 2, page 27
- Check that the children can partition when completing additions.

Number Workbook 2, page 29
- Check that the children can partition when completing subtractions.

Oral questions

Read each question twice. Allow about ten seconds after each reading.
1. What goes with eight to make ten?
2. What is seven add four?
3. What is nineteen take away nine?
4. What is thirteen subtract five?

Common difficulties

Children will need to be very secure in their addition bonds for all numbers up to 10 in order to use partitioning as a strategy in addition and subtraction. Practise these regularly.

The number line is a useful visual aid, as children will be able to see the next ten after a number. When adding 18 + 4, for example, it is clear that the next ten is twenty, so the answer is twenty and two more.

Practice activities

1 Deal a number card at random from a set (2 to 10). Write an addition that makes that number. Repeat for each card. Play again – try to think of different additions this time.

2 Split a set of number cards (1 to 20) into two piles: 1 to 10 and 11 to 20. Shuffle each set. Choose one card from each set and add them, writing the addition. Repeat until all the cards are gone. What are the different strategies you can use to complete each addition?

Answers

1. 2	**2.** 11	**3.** 10	**4.** 8
5. 18, 2, 4		**6.** 15, 5, 4	
7. 8	**8.** 4	**9.** 16	**10.** 27

11. 13 → 5, 24 → 16, 16 → 8, 26 → 18

Name _____

1. [ ]   **2.** [ ]   **3.** [ ]   **4.** [ ]

$\frac{\ }{4}$

Join 3 stars to make 24.

5.

6.

$\frac{\ }{4}$

Write the missing numbers.

7. $28 - \boxed{} = 20$ **8.** $14 - \boxed{} = 10$

9. $\boxed{} - 6 = 10$ **10.** $\boxed{} - 7 = 20$

$\frac{\ }{4}$

---

11. Join each balloon to the number 8 less.

16

5

8

18

$\frac{\ }{4}$

Score: [ ] /16   Total: [ ]

Fives and tens

Skills summary

- To count on and back in multiples of 10
- To count on in fives from zero
- To count back in fives to zero from a multiple of 5
- To understand and use the '×' sign
- To know ×10 multiplication facts
- To know ×5 multiplication facts

Diagnostic materials

Number Workbook 2, page 32
- Check that the children can count in fives.

Oral questions

Read each question twice. Allow about ten seconds after each reading.
1. What are three 5p coins worth?
2. Write the next number: five, ten, fifteen, twenty, ...
3. Seven fives are ...?
4. What is five lots of ten?

Common difficulties

Reinforce the meaning of the '×' sign, by reading it as 'lots of'. For children who have difficulty, set the multiplications in a practical context, e.g. reading 3 × 10 as three lots of 10 (e.g. three 10p coins, three strips of ten cubes).
For children who have difficulty remembering the facts, practice chanting the multiples of 5 and 10 regularly, using fingers to remember how many. Emphasise the repetitive nature of the chant (especially the multiples of 10).

Practice activities

1 Take a handful of 5p coins (up to ten). Count them: *five, ten, fifteen, ...* Write the matching multiplication, e.g. 4 × 5 = 20. Repeat with 10p coins.

2 Use number cards (5, 10, 15, ... 50). Select one at random. Say how many fives, e.g. *four fives are twenty*. Use coins to help, if necessary. Repeat for cards (10, 20, ... 100) and how many tens.

Answers

1. 15p	**2.** 25	**3.** 35	**4.** 50
5. 3	**6.** 40	**7.** 5	**8.** 5
9. 5	**10.** 7	**11.** 7	**12.** 10
13. 4 × 10	**14.** 9 × 5		

Name _____

1. ⬜   **2.** ⬜   **3.** ⬜   **4.** ⬜

$\boxed{}$ / 4

Write the missing numbers.

5. ⬜ x 5 = 15   **6.** 4 x 10 = ⬜

7. 6 x ⬜ = 30   **8.** 5 x ⬜ = 25

$\boxed{}$ / 4

Write the correct number of coins.

9. 25p ⬜ 5p coins   **10.** 35p ⬜ 5p coins

11. 70p ⬜ 10p coins   **12.** 100p ⬜ 10p coins

$\boxed{}$ / 4

Choose numbers to make each multiplication correct.

5   10   3   4   9   6

13. ⬜ x ⬜ = 40   **14.** ⬜ x ⬜ = 45

$\boxed{}$ / 4

Score: ⬜ /16   Total: ⬜

N26 Division

Sharing

Skills summary

- To understand and use the '÷' sign
- To sort small quantities into sets of equal size
- To divide a set of objects by sharing equally (no remainders)
- To begin to understand that some numbers cannot be shared equally

Diagnostic materials

Number Workbook 2, page 35
- Check that the children can share small quantities equally, in a practical context.

Oral questions

Read each question twice. Allow about ten seconds after each reading.
1. How many 5p coins make 20p?
2. If two children share eight sweets, how many will each get?
3. Can I share eight sweets equally among three children? Yes or no.
4. What is twelve divided into two equal groups?

Common difficulties

It is important at this stage to reinforce the practical context of division. For children who have difficulty encourage them to share small quantities (e.g. of counters) into two or three sets. Read divisions such as 6 ÷ 3 = as: *Six shared between three is...* The first number is the number of counters, the second is the number of sets.

Sharing into two sets can be related to counting in twos, and will start to give children a sense of those numbers that can be shared equally and those that can't.

Practice activities

1. Start with twelve small objects (e.g. plastic bears). Share them equally between two sets – how many in each set (write the matching division)? Share them equally between three sets, four sets, six sets. Extension: start with 24 bears.

2. Shuffle a set of cards (1 to 20). Deal them quickly into two piles: those that will divide equally by two and those that won't. You might want to check some of them at the end, using counters.

Answers			
1. 4	**2.** 4	**3.** No	**4.** 6
5. 3	**6.** 6	**7.** 5	**8.** 3
9. 4	**10.** 16 ÷ 2	**11.** 15 ÷ 3	

Name _____

I. [ ]   **2.** [ ]   **3.** [ ]   **4.** [ ]

$\dfrac{\square}{4}$

---

5. These sweets are shared among three.
   How many in each set?

$\dfrac{\square}{2}$

Complete these.

6. $12 \div 2 =$ [ ]   **7.** $10 \div 2 =$ [ ]

8. $15 \div 5 =$ [ ]   **9.** $12 \div 3 =$ [ ]

$\dfrac{\square}{4}$

Choose numbers to make each division correct.

10. [ ] $\div$ [ ] $= 8$ **II.** [ ] $\div$ [ ] $= 5$

$\dfrac{\square}{4}$

Score: [ ] /14   Total: [ ]

Fractions

Skills summary

- To recognise one half, one quarter or one third of a shape
- To find one half, one quarter or one third of a shape
- To recognise that two halves, three thirds, four quarters make one whole
- To use fraction notation, e.g. $\frac{1}{2}$, $\frac{1}{3}$

Diagnostic materials

Number Workbook 2, page 38
- Check that the children can recognise different simple fractions of shapes.

Oral questions

Draw four different shapes on the board, with halves, thirds or quarters shaded. Point to each shape in turn, asking whether a half, a third or a quarter is shaded.

Common difficulties

It is important that children understand that the two halves (or four quarters) should all be the same size. Reinforce by folding different shapes. Dividing into thirds may be more difficult, as it is not easy to demonstrate practically. Emphasise the fraction notation – the bottom number is the number of equal parts.

Practice activities

1 Draw a series of 4 × 4 grids. How many ways can you find of colouring a half? How many ways of colouring a quarter?

2 Draw a series of 3 × 6 grids. How many ways can you find of colouring a third?

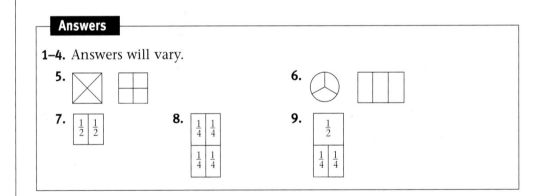

Answers

1–4. Answers will vary.

Name _____

N27

1.

2.

3.

4.

$\frac{}{4}$

5. Tick the shapes that have been divided into quarters.

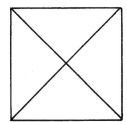 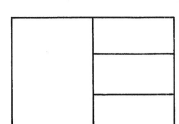 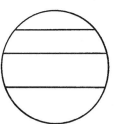 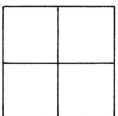

$\frac{}{4}$

6. Tick the shapes that have been divided into thirds.

 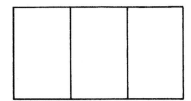 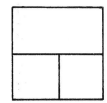 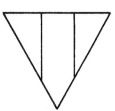

$\frac{}{4}$

Write the correct fraction in each part.

$\frac{1}{2}$ $\qquad$ $\frac{1}{3}$ $\qquad$ $\frac{1}{4}$

7.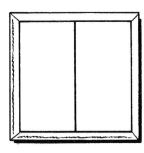

8.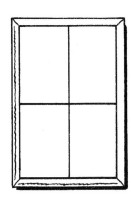

9.

$\frac{}{3}$

Score: [   ] /15   Total: [   ]

Numbers to 100

Skills summary

- To count a large number of objects by grouping in twos, fives or tens
- To estimate a number of objects
- To choose the more likely of two given estimates
- To say the larger and smaller of two given numbers (up to 100)
- To order three 1- or 2-digit numbers
- To order a set of given 1- and 2-digit numbers

Diagnostic materials

Number Workbook 3, page 2
- Check that the children can make sensible estimates of a number of objects.

Number Workbook 3, page 3
- Check that the children can order a set of numbers.

Oral questions

Read each question twice. Allow about ten seconds after each reading.

1. Are there more than twenty or less than twenty cubes? (Hold a handful of cubes in one hand.) Write 'm' or 'l'.

2. Which of these is the largest number? 61, 47, 38

3. Which of these is the smallest number? 58, 85, 15

4. Write a number between 27 and 35.

Common difficulties

Some children may find estimating difficult – help them by establishing a range (Is it less than 10? Is it more than 20? So, a good estimate would be…).

When ordering numbers, emphasise that children should look at the number of tens first, then the number of units.

Practice activities

1 Take a handful of coins and spread them out on the table. Write down an estimate of how much, then check by counting. Repeat.

2 Deal five cards at random from a set (1 to 100). How quickly can you place them in order? Repeat.

Answers

1. Answers will vary   **2.** 61   **3.** 15
4. 28 to 34   **5.** 20   **6.** 30   **7.** 20
8–11. Answers will vary
12. 5, 16, 19, 23, 32   **13.** 38, 21, 14, 12, 2

Name _____

1. [ ] **2.** [ ] **3.** [ ] **4.** [ ]

[ ]/4

Circle the estimate you think is closest.

5. 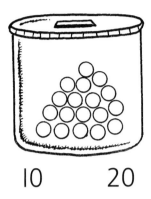 **6.** 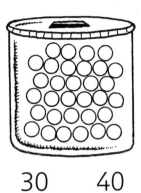 **7.**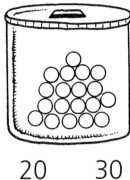

10   20   30   40   20   30

[ ]/3

Choose numbers so that each list is in order.

8. 28, [ ] , 42, 51   **9.** [ ] , 8, 23, 40

10. 4, [ ] , 7, [ ]   **11.** [ ] , 37, [ ] ,40

[ ]/4

Write these numbers in order.

16	23	5	19	32

12.

smallest   largest

21	14	12	38	2

13.

largest   smallest

[ ]/4

Score: [ ] /15   Total: [ ]

Addition and subtraction

Skills summary

- To know addition bonds to 10
- To know addition bonds to 20
- To know addition bonds for multiples of 10 to 100
- To recognise that numbers can be added in any order
- To add three 1-digit numbers (by looking for pairs that make 10, by putting the larger number first)

Diagnostic materials

Number Workbook 3, page 6

- Check that the children can use their knowledge of addition bonds to add three 1-digit numbers.

Oral questions

Read each question twice. Allow about ten seconds after each reading.
1. What goes with 14 to make 20?
2. How much more do I need to add to 30 to make 100?
3. What is 5 add 5 add 2?
4. What is the total of 7, 3 and 3?

Common difficulties

Provide plenty of practice for addition bonds to 10 and 20. Adding multiples of 10 to make 100 can be easily related to the addition bonds to 10.

When adding three numbers, emphasise that it is most efficient to start with the largest number first. Demonstrate, using cubes if necessary, that the order of addition makes no difference to the answer (i.e. $2 + 9 + 3$ is the same as $9 + 3 + 2$). For children who have difficulty with counting on (especially bridging the ten), use the number line as reinforcement.

Practice activities

1 Use number cards (0 to 20). Arrange them in pairs to make 20. Repeat for arranging them in threes.

2 How many ways are there of making '? + ? + ? = 12' correct? Try to be systematic. How many ways if the first number is 8?

Answers

1. 6	**2.** 70	**3.** 12	**4.** 13
5. 6p	**6.** 7p	**7.** 20p	
8. 3	**9.** 5	**10–11.** Answers will vary	
12. 6, 4 or 2, 8		**13.** 5, 2	
14. 16, 4, 2		**15.** 16, 8, 2 or 16, 4, 6	

Name _____

1. [ ]   **2.** [ ]   **3.** [ ]   **4.** [ ]

$\dfrac{\square}{4}$

Write how much change.

5. 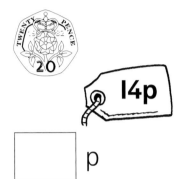 14p
[ ] p

6. 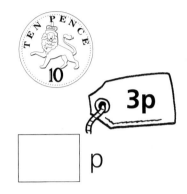 3p
[ ] p

7. 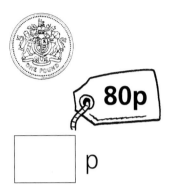 80p
[ ] p

$\dfrac{\square}{3}$

Write the missing numbers..

8. $6 + \boxed{} + 1 = 10$

9. $9 + \boxed{} + 6 = 20$

10. $15 = \boxed{} + \boxed{} + 5$

11. $24 = \boxed{} + \boxed{} + 3$

$\dfrac{\square}{4}$

Choose numbers to make these correct.

6   4   5   2   8   16

12. $\boxed{} + \boxed{} + 8 = 18$ **13.** $5 + \boxed{} + \boxed{} = 12$

14. $\boxed{} + \boxed{} + \boxed{} = 22$ **15.** $26 = \boxed{} + \boxed{} + \boxed{}$

$\dfrac{\square}{4}$

Score: [ ] /15   Total: [ ]

Doubling

Skills summary

- To double numbers by adding
- To know doubles for numbers up to 15
- To know doubles of multiples of 5 to 50
- To know addition bonds for multiples of 10 to 100

Diagnostic materials

Number Workbook 3, page 13
- Check that the children are able to double numbers up to 15.

Oral questions

Read each question twice. Allow about ten seconds after each reading.
1. What is double eight?
2. Double 25.
3. What is 40 add 40?
4. Mary is 8. John is twice her age. How old is John?

Common difficulties

Doubles of numbers 6 to 9 are more difficult to remember – provide plenty of practice.
For children who have difficulty doubling larger numbers, help by adding in two stages, doubling the tens first (e.g. double 25 is 20 + 20 + 5 + 5).

Practice activities

1 Deal a number card at random from a set (1 to 10). Say its double. Continue. How quickly can you work through the set?

2 Work with a partner. Take a handful of 10p and 5 coins. Find the total and write it. Your partner matches your coins, and together you find the new total. Write it as double the first total.

Answers			
1. 16	**2.** 50	**3.** 80	**4.** 16
5. 4p	**6.** 20p	**7.** 10p	**8.** 100p
9. 6	**10.** 8	**11.** 15	**12.** 25 + 25
13. ✓	**14.** ✗	**15.** ✗	**16.** ✓

Name _____

I. [ ]   **2.** [ ]   **3.** [ ]   **4.** [ ]

[ ]
/4

Write the totals

5. [ ] p   **6.**  [ ] p

7. [ ] p   **8.**  [ ] p

[ ]
/4

Write the missing numbers.

9. [ ] + 6 = 12   **10.** 8 + [ ] = 16

II. 15 + [ ] = 30   **12.** 50 = [ ] + [ ]

[ ]
/4

Tick the sentences that are correct.

13. double 9 is 18 [ ]   **14.** double 35 is 65 [ ]

15. 24 is double II [ ]   **16.** 80 is double 40 [ ]

[ ]
/4

Score: [ ] /16   Total: [ ]

Difference

Skills summary

- To find the difference between two small quantities by counting unmatched objects
- To find the difference between two 1-digit numbers by counting on from the smaller to the larger
- To find the difference between two 2-digit numbers by counting on from the smaller to the larger (not bridging a ten)
- To find the difference between two 1-digit numbers by counting on from the smaller to the larger (bridging a ten)

Diagnostic materials

Number Workbook 3, page 15

- Check that the children can find differences between small numbers of objects in a practical context.

Oral questions

Read each question twice. Allow about ten seconds after each reading.

1. If Jo has four sweets and Faye has six sweets, how many more sweets does Faye have?
2. Raj has seven sweets, how many more does he need to make ten?
3. What is the difference between 10 and 14?
4. What is the difference between 18 and 23?

Common difficulties

For children who have difficulty with the concept of difference, focus on practical contexts – strips of cubes provide an excellent visual aid. Help focus the children by asking questions such as: *How many more cubes in this strip?*

Difference can also be reinforced by matching pairs of items, e.g. matching each blue cube to a yellow cube: *How many yellow cubes are left over?*

The language of difference will also arise in many measuring contexts, e.g. length, weight.

Practice activities

1 Take a handful of interlocking cubes (blue) and build a strip. Take another handful (yellow) and build a second strip. What is the difference between the two strips? Are there more blue or yellow cubes? How many more?

2 Deal two cards at random from a set (15 to 25). What is the difference between the two numbers? Use cubes to help. Write a matching subtraction.

Answers

1. 2	**2.** 3	**3.** 4	**4.** 5
5. 4 cm	**6.** 3 cm	**7.** 8 cm	**8.** 6 cm
9. 13 m	**10.** 22 m	**11.** 11 m	**12.** 24 m

Name _____

| 1. [   ] | 2. [   ] | 3. [   ] | 4. [   ] |

$\dfrac{\square}{4}$

Write the difference in length between each pair.

5.  16 cm

 12 cm

difference = [   ] cm

6.  14 cm

 11 cm

difference = [   ] cm

7.  22 cm

 14 cm

difference = [   ] cm

8.  24 cm

18 cm

difference = [   ] cm

$\dfrac{\square}{4}$

The difference between each pair is 5 metres.
Write the shorter length.

9.  [   ] m   18 m

10.  [   ] m   27 m

11.  [   ] m   16 m

12.  [   ] m   29 m

$\dfrac{\square}{4}$

Score: [   ] /12   Total: [   ]

3-digit numbers

Skills summary

- To recite the number names, in order, to 1000 and beyond
- To say the number one more or one less than a given 2- or 3-digit number
- To say the larger and smaller of two given 2- or 3-digit numbers
- To order a set of 2- and 3-digit numbers
- To round a 2-digit number to its nearest ten

Diagnostic materials

Number Workbook 3, page 18
- Check that the children are able to read and write 3-digit numbers.

Number Workbook 3, page 20
- Check that the children understand place-value in 3-digit numbers.

Oral questions

Read each question twice. Allow about ten seconds after each reading.
1. Write this number: 106.
2. Write the number that comes after 199.
3. Write the number that comes before 310.
4. Write the number that is the nearest ten to 42.

Common difficulties

When reading 3-digit numbers, children who have difficulty should first cover up the hundreds digit and read the remaining 2-digit number. They can then 'add' the hundreds separately. This will help children focus on the difference between 315 and 351, for example, and will also help when ordering.

For children who have difficulty with writing 3-digit numbers, or with place-value, provide plenty of concrete examples, e.g. money, base-ten equipment. Start first by matching numbers with hundreds, tens and units. Move on to numbers that have a zero in either the tens or units place.

Rounding to the nearest ten can be assisted by using a number line, or grid where children can see the nearest ten. Remind children that 2-digit numbers with 5 units round up to the next ten.

Practice activities

1 Take a handful of coins from each of three piles (£1, 10p, 1p). Arrange them under headings: H, T, U, and write the matching number. After ten rounds, write all the numbers in order – use coins to help, if necessary. Repeat, selecting coins from two piles only.

2 Throw a dice twice to create a 2-digit number (the first throw for tens the second for units). Write it, then round it to the nearest ten (use a number grid to help).

Answers

1. 106	**2.** 200	**3.** 309	**4.** 40
5. 139, 141	**6.** 280, 281	**7.** 899, 901	**8.** 498, 500
9. 407, 414, 425, 438			
10. 30	**11.** 40	**12.** 60	**13.** 80

Name _____

1. ☐   **2.** ☐   **3.** ☐   **4.** ☐

☐/4

Write the missing numbers.

5. | 140 |

6. | 279 |

7. | 900 |

8. | 499 |

☐/4

9. Write the number in each cloud.

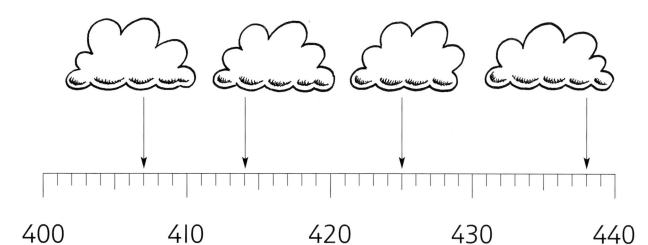

400   410   420   430   440

☐/4

Write each of these to the nearest 10.

10. 27 ⟶ ☐   **11.** 43 ⟶ ☐

12. 55 ⟶ ☐   **13.** 81 ⟶ ☐

☐/4

Abacus Ginn and Company 1999.
Copying permitted for purchasing school only.
This material is not copyright free.

Score: ☐ /16   Total: ☐

Doubling and halving

Skills summary

- To double a number (up to 10) by adding
- To know doubles of numbers to 15
- To know doubles of multiples of 5 to 50
- To understand halving as the inverse of doubling
- To use doubles when adding

Diagnostic materials

Number Workbook 3, page 21

- Check that the children understand the relationship between doubling and having.

Oral questions

Read each question twice. Allow about ten seconds after each reading.

1. What is double 8?
2. What is half of 12?
3. Double 45.
4. Leon is 35 years old. Jade is twice his age. How old is she?

Common difficulties

Doubles of numbers 6 to 9 are more difficult to remember – provide plenty of practice.

For children who have difficulty doubling larger numbers, help by adding in two stages, doubling the tens first (e.g. double 25 is 20 + 20 + 5 + 5). Halving a larger number can be approached in a similar way.

Practise doubles regularly, and remind children to look out for doubles or near-doubles when adding.

Practice activities

1 Use place-value cards (tens and units). Shuffle the tens and deal them one at a time. Say half of each number, and match it using tens and units cards.

2 Use a number grid (1 to 100). Choose two 'next-door' numbers at random and add them. Try to use doubling to help.

Answers			
1. 16	**2.** 6	**3.** 90	**4.** 70
5. 12 cm	**6.** 26 cm	**7.** 40 cm	**8.** 70 cm
9. 25	**10.** 7	**11.** 11	**12.** 45
13. 7	**14.** 6	**15.** 9	**16.** 8

Name _____

I. [ ] **2.** [ ] **3.** [ ] **4.** [ ]

[ ]
―
4

Double each length.

5.  [ ] cm
6 cm

6. [ ] cm
13 cm

7. [ ] cm
20 cm

8. [ ] cm
35 cm

[ ]
―
4

Write the missing numbers.

9. double [ ] = 50   **10.** double [ ] = 14

II. double [ ] = 22   **12.** double [ ] = 90

[ ]
―
4

Complete these.

13. 13 = 6 + [ ]   **14.** 5 + [ ] = 11

15. 8 + [ ] = 17   **16.** 15 = 7 + [ ]

[ ]
―
4

Score: [ ] /16   Total: [ ]

Addition and subtraction

Skills summary

- To understand the relationship between addition and subtraction
- To know the subtraction fact for a given addition fact
- To know the addition fact for a given subtraction fact

Diagnostic materials

Number Workbook 3, page 28

- Check that the children understand the relationship between addition and subtraction.

Oral questions

Read each question twice. Allow about ten seconds after each reading.

1. 16 add what makes 24?

2. You have 50p and the yo-yo costs 34p. How much change?

3. The lolly cost 45p and I was given 5p change. How much money did I give the shopkeeper?

4. 28 take away what leaves 14?

Common difficulties

Some children may use counting on and back instead of other more efficient strategies. Encourage them to try and use addition bonds etc. when solving calculations. Individual pupil number lines or grids can help them visualise adding to the next ten etc.

Encourage links between addition and subtraction by presenting children with 'missing number' calculations, e.g. 3 + ? = 10, 14 – ? = 8.

Practice activities

1 How many different additions and subtractions can you write using 7, 3 and 10? Repeat for other trios, e.g. 8, 4, 12 or 16, 4, 20.

2 Take two handfuls of coins. How many different ways can you find of making the two amounts equal? Use additions and subtractions – use more than one at a time.

Answers

1. 8	**2.** 16p	**3.** 50p	**4.** 14
5. 7p	**6.** 27p	**7.** 4p	

8. 8 + 4 = 12, 12 – 4 = 8, 4 + 8 = 12, 12 – 8 = 4
16 + 5 = 21, 21 – 5 = 16, 5 + 16 = 21, 21 – 16 = 5

9. 29p

Name _____

1. [ ]   2. [ ]   3. [ ]   4. [ ]

[ ]/4

Write how much change.

5. **13p**

[ ] p

6. 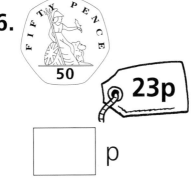 **23p**

[ ] p

7.  **6p**

[ ] p

[ ]/3

8. Choose numbers to make the calculations correct.

 £8 £12 £4   £21 £5 £16

[ ] + [ ] = [ ]   [ ] + [ ] = [ ]

[ ] − [ ] = [ ]   [ ] − [ ] = [ ]

[ ]/4

9. James buys a comic and crisps, with £1. Write how much change he gets.

 **43p**   **28p**

[ ] p

[ ]/4

Score: [ ] /15   Total: [ ]

Multiplication and division

Skills summary

- To understand multiplication through the use of arrays
- To recognise that two numbers can be multiplied in any order
- To understand the relationship between multiplication and division
- To understand division as 'how many lots of...?'
- To divide a number of objects by grouping (no remainders)
- To use the '×' and '÷' signs

Diagnostic materials

Number Workbook 3, page 33
- Check that the children can solve multiplications in a practical context.

Number Workbook 3, page 36
- Check that the children can solve divisions in a practical context.

Oral questions

Read each question twice. Allow about ten seconds after each reading.
1. How many 5p coins are worth 25p?
2. What are six twos?
3. How many fours in sixteen?
4. Multiply five by five.

Common difficulties

Reinforce the meaning of the '×' sign by reading it as 'lots of'. For children who have difficulty, set the multiplications in a practical context (e.g. using cubes, counters). Use grids to represent the multiplications – turning these will reinforce the commutativity of multiplication.

Dividing by grouping has close links with multiplication – read the '÷' sign as 'how many lots in'.

Practice activities

1 Select two cards at random from a set (1 to 10). Write two multiplications using the two numbers and draw a grid on squared paper for each.

2 Take a handful of 5p coins. Find the total and write a division to match, e.g. 20p ÷ 4 = 5p. Repeat.

Answers

1. 5	**2.** 12	**3.** 4	**4.** 25
5. 12	**6.** 4	**7.** 4	**8.** 3

9. $3 \times 5 = 15$, $15 \div 3 = 5$, $5 \times 3 = 15$, $5 \div 5 = 3$
$4 \times 5 = 20$, $20 \div 4 = 5$, $5 \times 4 = 20$, $20 \div 5 = 4$

10. 3   **11.** 4

Name _____

I. [ ]   **2.** [ ]   **3.** [ ]   **4.** [ ]

$\frac{}{4}$

Complete these.

5. 4 lots of 3 = [ ]   **6.** 2 lots of [ ] = 8

7. [ ] lots of 4 = 16   **8.** 3 lots of [ ] = 9

$\frac{}{4}$

9. Choose numbers to make the calculations correct.

[ ] × [ ] = [ ]   [ ] × [ ] = [ ]

[ ] ÷ [ ] = [ ]   [ ] ÷ [ ] = [ ]

$\frac{}{4}$

Kay has 36p. How many of each can she buy?

10. pencil 12p

II. rubber 9p

$\frac{}{4}$

Score: [ ] /16   Total: [ ]

Fractions

Skills summary

- To find one half, one quarter, one third of a shape
- To find one half, one quarter, one third of a given number of objects by sharing into equal sets
- To recognise that two quarters are the same as one half
- To use fraction notation

Diagnostic materials

Number Workbook 3, page 38
- Check that the children can find half of a quantity.

Oral questions

Read each question twice. Allow about ten seconds after each reading.
1. What is half of six?
2. Write one half of twelve.
3. What is sixteen halved?
4. If I have twelve sweets and eat one quarter of them, how many do I eat?

Common difficulties

Children are more likely to have difficulty halving and quartering a number of objects rather than a shape or object. A good bridge between shapes and quantities is to use grids. Start with a 4 × 2 grid, and colour one row of four squares – one half (so, one half of eight is four). Repeat for colouring a column of two squares – one quarter (so one quarter of eight is two). Use other grids to extend this idea, e.g. 4 × 4, 4 × 5, 4 × 6. When children are confident working with grids, they can move on to discrete objects (e.g. cubes) arranged in regular arrays.

Practice activities

1 Draw a series of 4 × 4 grids. How many ways can you find of colouring a half? How many ways of colouring a quarter? Repeat for a 4 × 6 grid.

2 Use cubes or counters. Take a handful. Can you halve the number? What is one half? Can you quarter the number? What is one quarter? Try placing the cubes in an array to help you.

Answers			
1. 3	**2.** 6	**3.** 8	**4.** 3
5. 6 squares coloured		**6.** 4 squares coloured	
7. 5	**8.** 9	**9.** 10	**10.** 24
11. $\frac{1}{4}$	**12.** $\frac{1}{2}$		

Name _____

1. [ ]   **2.** [ ]   **3.** [ ]   **4.** [ ]

$\dfrac{}{4}$

5. Colour more squares to cover one half of the shape.

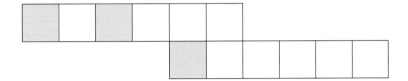

$\dfrac{}{2}$

6. Colour more squares to cover one quarter of the shape.

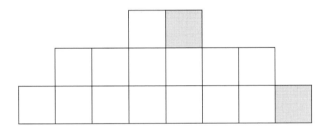

$\dfrac{}{2}$

Write the missing numbers.

7. $\frac{1}{4}$ of 20 = [ ]   **8.** $\frac{1}{2}$ of 18 = [ ]

9. $\frac{1}{2}$ of [ ] = 5   **10.** $\frac{1}{4}$ of [ ] = 6

11. $\dfrac{[\ \ ]}{[\ \ ]}$ of 8 = 2   **12.** $\dfrac{[\ \ ]}{[\ \ ]}$ of 20 = 10

$\dfrac{}{6}$

Score: [ ] /14   Total: [ ]

M1 **M2** Length

Length

Skills summary

- To measure lengths using a non-standard unit
- To recognise metres and centimetres as standard units
- To measure lengths in centimetres and metres
- To estimate lengths in centimetres and metres
- To recognise the relationship between centimetres and metres

Diagnostic materials

Shape, Space and Measures Workbook, page 1
- Check that the children can use a ruler correctly and can measure in centimetres.

Shape, Space and Measures Workbook, page 3
- Check children recognise the need for metres when measuring long lengths.

Oral questions

Read each question twice. Allow about ten seconds after each reading.
1. Estimate the length of this line in centimetres. (Draw a 10 cm line on the board.)
2. How many centimetres in a metre?
3. 3 metres is how many centimetres?
4. Do you think the height of the door is more or less than a metre?
Note: Children will need a ruler to complete this sheet.

Common difficulties

Using a ruler correctly is difficult. Use a ruler with the zero at the very end, so that children do not have to align the base-line. Emphasise that each mark refers to one more centimetre. Encourage them to estimate where the object ends, e.g. six and a bit centimetres.

Emphasise that estimating is about making a sensible guess – nobody will be completely accurate. It is worth first of all establishing a range, before making an estimate (e.g. is the ruler more than 5 centimetres? Is it less than 20 centimetres? So a good estimate is ... 12 centimetres).

A class height chart will allow the children to become accustomed to measuring and comparing their own heights

Practice activities

1 Use a selection of objects (sticks, lengths of string or ribbon, pencils, etc.). Sort them into two sets: more than 10 cm, less than 10 cm. Measure any you are unsure about. Sort them again for: more than 20 cm, less than 20 cm.

2 Use a selection of objects (sticks, lengths of string or ribbon, pencils, paint brushes etc.). Sort them into several sets: between 0 cm and 5 cm, between 5 cm and 10 cm, between 10 cm and 15 cm, ... Measure them all to check.

Answers

1. Accept an estimate between 8 and 12 cm

2. 100	**3.** 300	**4.** More	**5.** Check line
6. a	**7.** 100	**8.** 200	**9.** 50
10. 3	**11.** 20 cm		

Name _____

1. [ ]   **2.** [ ]   **3.** [ ]   **4.** [ ]

$\dfrac{}{4}$

5. Draw a line 8 cm long.

$\dfrac{}{2}$

6. Tick the line that is 10 cm long.

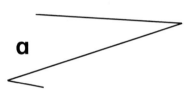

a   b   c

$\dfrac{}{2}$

Write the missing numbers.

7. 1 m = [ ] cm   **8.** 2 m = 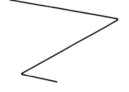 cm

9. $\frac{1}{2}$ m = [ ] cm   **10.** 300 cm [ ] m

$\dfrac{}{4}$

11. Circle how long you think the line is.

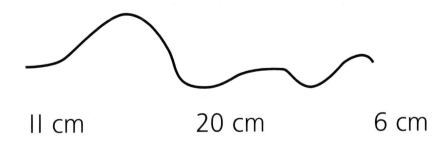

11 cm   20 cm   6 cm

$\dfrac{}{2}$

Score: [ ] /14   Total: [ ]

M3 **M4** **M7** Time

Time

Skills summary

- To recognise 'o'clock' times on digital and analogue clocks
- To understand 'past' and 'to' the hour
- To recognise 'quarter past', 'quarter to' and 'half past' times on digital and analogue clocks
- To use the vocabulary related to time

Diagnostic materials

Shape, Space and Measures Workbook, page 14
- Check that the children can tell the time to the hour and half hour on analogue and digital clocks.

Shape, Space and Measures Workbook, page 15
- Check that the children can read an analogue clock showing quarter to and quarter past the hour.

Oral questions

Read each question twice. Allow about ten seconds after each reading.
1. Write 3 o'clock as a digital time.
2. How many minutes in one hour?
3. Write the digital time for 'half past 4'.
4. Write the digital time for 'quarter past 7'.

Common difficulties

Telling the time is very difficult, and it is important that children understand the difference between the hour and minute hands. Provide plenty of practice of telling the time, on both analogue and digital clocks. Focus on the fact that each major division on an analogue clock is equal to five minutes – as the minute (big) hand moves from one division to the next, five minutes has passed (counting in fives is a key pre-requisite skill).

Practice activities

1. Use an analogue clock with movable hands. Throw a dice and set the hour hand to match. Set the minute hand to show quarter past, half past and quarter to, recording each time as a digital time.

2. Use two sets of number cards (1 to 12) and (15, 30, 45). Select one card from each pile at random to make a digital time. Say it aloud, and record it.

Answers

1. 3:00	**2.** 60	**3.** 4:30	**4.** 7:15
5. (clock) `7:45`		**6.** 30	**7.** 15
8. 60	**9.** 45	**10.** (clock)	**11.** `9:15`

Name _____

I. [   ]   **2.** [   ]   **3.** [   ]   **4.** [   ]

[ ]/4

5. Draw and write the time 'quarter to 8'.

   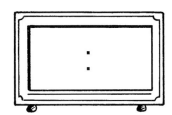

[ ]/4

Write the missing numbers.

6. $\frac{1}{2}$ hour = [   ] minutes   **7.** $\frac{1}{4}$ hour = [   ] minutes

8. I hour = [   ] minutes   **q.** $\frac{3}{4}$ hour = [   ] minutes

[ ]/4

Show the times half an hour later.

10.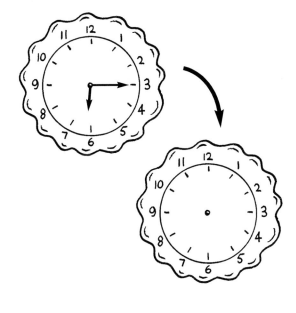

II.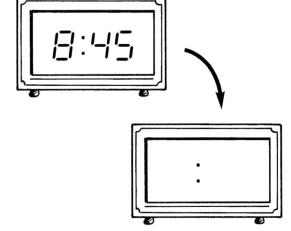

[ ]/4

Score: [   ] /16   Total: [   ]

Weight

Skills summary

- To measure weights using a non-standard unit
- To recognise the need for a standard unit of weight
- To recognise kilograms and grams as a standard unit of weight
- To estimate and measure weights in kilograms and grams

Diagnostic materials

Shape, Space and Measures Workbook, page 6
- Check that the children can measure the weight of several objects in a practical context.

Oral questions

Read each question twice. Allow about ten seconds after each reading.
1. How many grams in a kilogram?
2. Hold up a bag of potatoes. What would you use to weigh these, grams or kilograms?
3. What would you use to weigh yourself?
4. Hold up a potato and ask, more than a kilogram or less than a kilogram?

Common difficulties

Children may find estimating the weight of an object difficult – large objects are sometimes light. Encourage them to feel the objects, and establish a range (e.g. is it more than 100 g? Is it less than a kilogram?).

Children need to realise that there is a technique to using a balance. The objects to be weighed go in one pan, and then are left untouched (i.e. if weighing a set of pencils, no pencils should be removed to make the scales balance). Weights should then be placed in the second pan (starting with larger weights, and moving successively to lighter ones).

Practice activities

1 Can you make a plasticine snake to balance with 100 g? How many snakes do you need to balance with a kilogram?

2 Fill several yoghurt pots to the same level with different materials, e.g. sand, pasta, rice, counters. Can you order the pots by weight? Which pot do you think is the lightest/heaviest? Can you balance these pots?

Answers

1. 1000	**2.** kg	**3.** kg	**4.** less
5. banana	**6.** orange	**7.** 72 g	**8.** g
9. kg	**10.** kg	**11.** g	

Name _____

I. [ ]   **2.** [ ]   **3.** [ ]   **4.** [ ]

[ ] / 4

apple 34 g

orange 43 g

banana 29 g

pear 38 g

5. Which fruit is lightest? _____

6. Which fruit is heaviest? _____

[ ] / 2

7. What is the total weight of the orange and banana?

[   ] g

[ ] / 2

What unit would you use to weigh each item?
Write kg or g.

8. 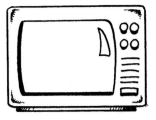 [ ]   **q.**  [ ]

10.  [ ]   **II.**  [ ]

[ ] / 4

Score: [   ] / 12   Total: [   ]

Capacity

Skills summary

- To measure capacities using a non-standard unit
- To recognise the need for a standard unit of capacity
- To recognise litres as a standard unit of capacity
- To estimate and measure capacities in litres
- To compare the capacities of different containers by measuring
- To recognise the need for calibration
- To measure capacity using a calibrated container
- To calibrate a container using a non-standard unit

Diagnostic materials

Shape, Space and Measures workbook, page 7
- Check that the children can measure capacity in a practical context.

Oral questions

Read each question twice. Allow about ten seconds after each reading.
1. Does the red bucket or the yellow bucket hold more? (Hold up two buckets of different sizes and colours.)
2. Do you think this bottle holds more than a litre or less than a litre? (Hold up a milk bottle.)
3. How many pots do you think the mug will hold? (Hold up a mug and a yoghurt pot.)
4. Do you think this carton holds more than a litre or less than a litre? (Hold up a small drinks carton.)

Common difficulties

Ensure children have a variety of practical experiences measuring and comparing capacities (e.g. comparing tall and short containers – the taller does not always hold the most). Focus on key vocabulary: full, half-full, empty, and encourage children to use it correctly.

Children should have plenty of experience of calibrating containers, using a non-standard unit (e.g. yoghurt pots). They can measure the capacity of a variety of objects using their calibrated container.

Practice activities

1 Measure the capacity of the same container using different fillers, e.g. sand, water, rice. The capacity is the same, despite the different fillers.

2 Use a calibrated container, e.g. a jug. Choose a different container, fill it, and empty it into the jug. Estimate first (by sticking tape on the jug).

Answers

1–4. Answers will vary.
  5. 1 litre   6. a. 8   b. 4   c. 30
  7. no   8. 2   9. 12

1. [ ]   **2.** [ ]   **3.** [ ]   **4.** [ ]

□/4

---

5. Join the bottle to the correct label.

| I centimetre |
| I metre |
| I litre |

| I hour |
| I kilogram |

□/2

---

6. Write how much in each container.

a 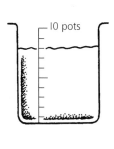   _10 pots_

b 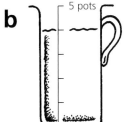   _5 pots_

c 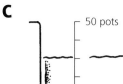   _50 pots_

[ ] pots   [ ] pots   [ ] pots

□/3

7. Will the water in **c** fit in **a**?   yes [ ]   no [ ]

8. How many more pots to fill **a**?   [ ] pots

9. What is the total amount in **a** and **b**?   [ ] pots

□/3

Score: [ ] /12   Total: [ ]

Time

Skills summary

- To know and order the months of the year
- To relate particular months to the appropriate seasons
- To recognise seconds, minutes, hours as standard measures of time
- To recognise days, weeks, months, years as standard measures of time
- To recognise the relationships between different units of time

Diagnostic materials

Shape, Space and Measures Workbook, page 17
- Check that the children can order the months.

Shape, Space and Measures Workbook, page 21
- Check that the children know relationships between standard units of time.

Oral questions

Read each question twice. Allow about ten seconds after each reading.
1. How many days in a week?
2. How many hours in a day?
3. What unit would you use to measure your age?
4. What unit would you use to time eating your breakfast?

Common difficulties

The vocabulary of time may be used quite loosely in conversation and it is important that children understand the various terms and can use them accurately. Time the children during various activities, using Blu-tack to mark a clock. Telling the time is very difficult and it is important that children understand the difference between the hour and minute hands. Provide plenty of practice of telling the time, on both analogue and digital clocks. Focus on the fact that each major division on an analogue clock is equal to five minutes – as the minute (big) hand moves from one division to the next, five minutes has passed (counting in fives is a key pre-requisite skill).

Relate months of the year to dates that are important to the children: birthdays, Christmas, etc. Practice chanting the months in order, until the children are confident.

Practice activities

1 Make a display of all the time relationships you know: between seconds and minutes, minutes and hours, hours and days etc. You might want to extend this to include seconds in an hour etc. (Use a calculator to help.)

2 Conduct a survey to find which month each child in the class has their birthday. Record them in a table – write the months in order, and next to each the number of children. Which month had most children?

Answers

1. 7	**2.** 24	**3.** years	**4.** minutes
5. April	**6.** June	**7.** September	
8. 120	**9.** 30	**10.** 14	**11.** 12

12. August → summer, April → spring, October → autumn, January → winter

---

Name _____

1. [ ]   **2.** [ ]   **3.** [ ]   **4.** [ ]

$\boxed{} \over 4$

Write the missing months. Choose from the list.

June   April   September

5. February, March, _____

6. May, _____, July

7. _____, October, November

$\boxed{} \over 3$

Write the missing numbers.

8. 2 minutes = [ ] seconds   **9.** $\frac{1}{2}$ minute = [ ] seconds

10. 2 weeks = [ ] days   **11.** [ ] years = 24 months

$\boxed{} \over 4$

12. Join each month to the correct season.

August   summer

April   winter

October   autumn

January   spring

$\boxed{} \over 4$

Score: [ ] /15   Total: [ ]

3-d shape

Skills summary

- To recognise and name common 3-d shapes: cubes, cuboids, pyramids, spheres
- To recognise and name cylinders and cones
- To describe the properties of common 3-d shapes
- To sort 3-d shapes according to type of face (flat, curved, square, rectangular etc.)

Diagnostic materials

Shape, Space and Measures Workbook, page 23

- Check that the children recognise common 3-d shapes.

Oral questions

Read each question twice. Allow about ten seconds after each reading.

1. Write the name of this shape (hold up a cube). *cube*
2. What shape has four triangle-faces? *Cuboid.*
3. How many faces does this shape have (hold up a square-based pyramid)? *cylinder*
4. What is the name of this shape (hold up a cylinder)? *sphere*

Common difficulties

When working with 3-d shapes it is important that children have concrete examples to help them. Focus on the types of face: squares, rectangles, triangles. Encourage children to build shapes using construction equipment (e.g. Polydron), which they can then take apart to compare and count the faces.

Practice activities

1 Use construction equipment (e.g. Polydron). How many different solid shapes can you make using only six pieces of Polydron? Name each shape, and describe its faces. Repeat for eight pieces.

2 Cut different pictures out of a catalogue or magazine. Name some of the shapes you can see (use solid shapes to help).

Answers

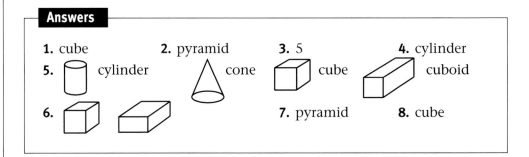

1. cube   2. pyramid   3. 5   4. cylinder
5. cylinder   cone   cube   cuboid
6.   7. pyramid   8. cube

Name _____

1. [_____]   2. [_____]   3. [_____]   4. [_____]

$\frac{\Box}{4}$

5. Join each shape to the correct name.

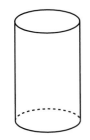  

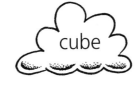

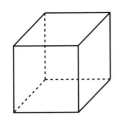 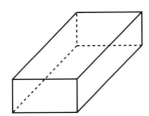

$\frac{\Box}{4}$

6. Circle the shapes with 6 faces.

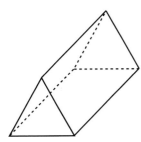 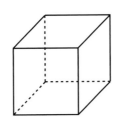 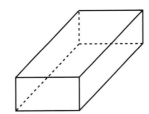 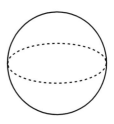

$\frac{\Box}{4}$

Write the names of the shapes you can make with these faces.

7. 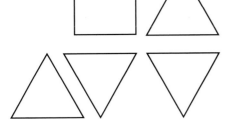   **8.**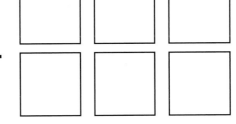

_____   _____

$\frac{\Box}{4}$

Score: [____] /16   Total: [_____]

Angle

Skills summary

- To recognise clockwise and anticlockwise turns
- To describe or follow a route using clockwise and anticlockwise turns
- To recognise angle as a measure of turn
- To recognise and construct a right-angle
- To measure a right-angle using a template

Diagnostic materials

Shape, Space and Measures Workbook, page 24
- Check that the children can recognise clockwise and anticlockwise turns.

Shape, Space and Measures Workbook, page 26
- Check that the children can recognise right-angles.

Oral questions

Read each question twice. Allow about ten seconds after each reading.
Draw these on the board, asking a question about each:

1. A rectangle. How many right-angles in this shape?
2. A right-angled triangle. How many right-angles in this shape?
3. An arrow moving in a clockwise direction. Is this turn clockwise or anticlockwise? Write 'c' or 'a'.
4. An acute angle. Is this more or less than a right-angle?

Common difficulties

Help children to remember clockwise and anticlockwise by referring to the hands on a clock. Use the vocabulary in different situations (e.g. PE, lining up).

Children will need to be given plenty of practice recognising right-angles. Ensure they realise that the right-angles can be in different orientations (e.g. a ⌐ is a right-angle, even though it faces left). Encourage children to look for right-angles in the classroom (e.g. table corners, book corners), testing each with a template.

Practice activities

1 Draw a route on squared paper. Describe each turn as clockwise or anticlockwise.

2 Design and colour a pattern with lots of right-angles. Draw the right-angles in different orientations. Make a display.

Answers

1. 4	**2.** 1	**3.** c	**4.** less
5–8. check arrows	**9.** 4	**10.** 2	**11.** 0
12. 3	**13.** a, c		

Name _____

1. [ ]   **2.** [ ]   **3.** [ ]   **4.** [ ]

$\frac{\square}{4}$

Draw an arrow on each windmill to match the label.

5.    **6.**    **7.**    **8.**

| clockwise | anticlockwise | clockwise | anticlockwise |

$\frac{\square}{4}$

Write how many right-angles in each shape.

9. [ ] right-angles

10. 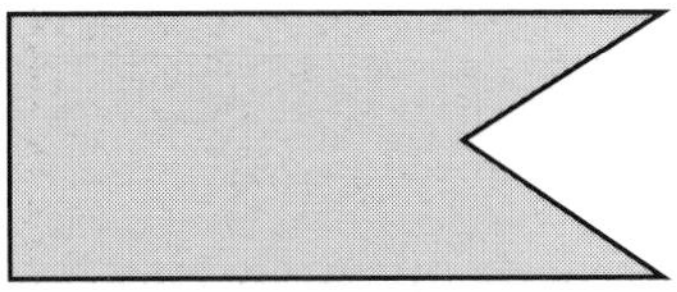 [ ] right-angles

11. 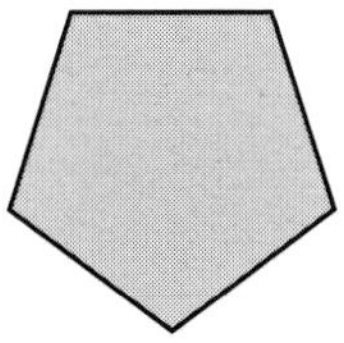 [ ] right-angles

12. 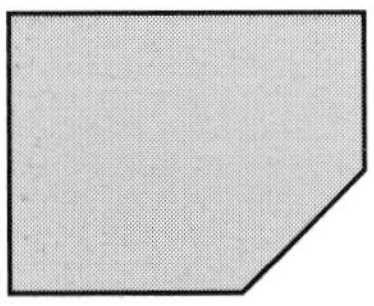 [ ] right-angles

$\frac{\square}{4}$

13. Tick the angles that are less than a right-angle.

a   b   c   d

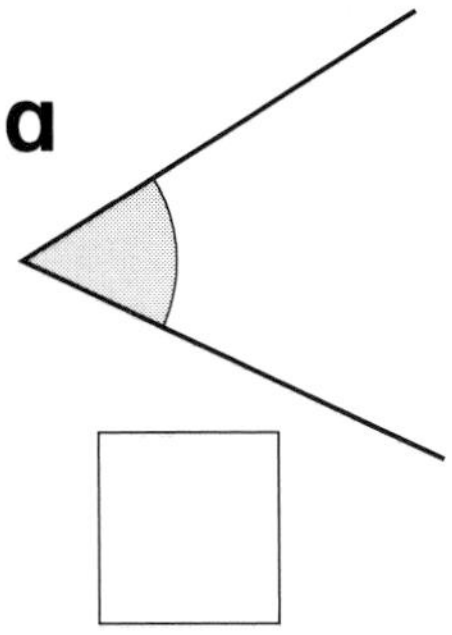

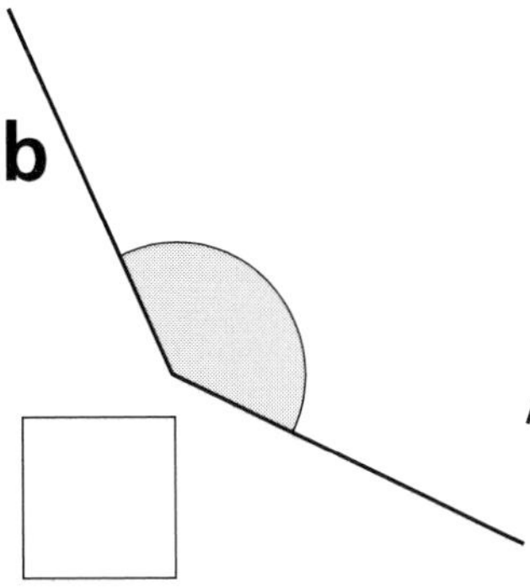

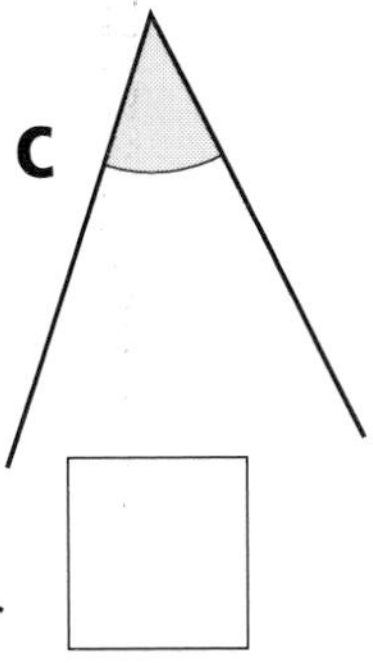

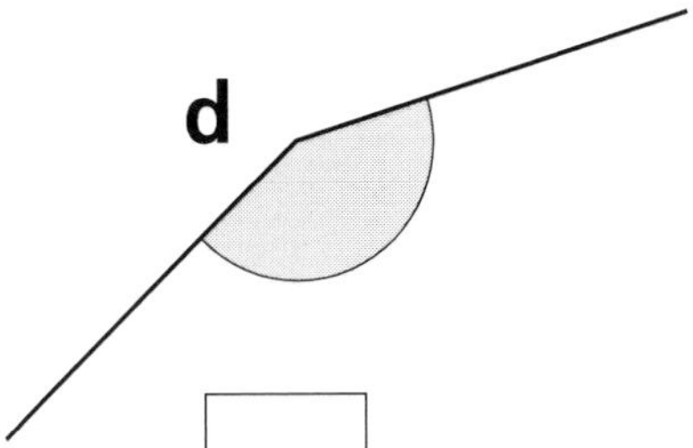

[ ]   [ ]   [ ]   [ ]

$\frac{\square}{2}$

Score: [ ] /14   Total: [ ]

2-d shape

Skills summary

- To recognise and name common 2-d shapes: square, rectangle, triangle, circle
- To recognise and name pentagons, hexagons, octagons
- To describe the properties of 2-d shapes
- To sort 2-d shapes according to number of sides or corners (vertices)

Diagnostic materials

Shape, Space and Measures Workbook, page 28
- Check that the children can recognise and name common 2-d shapes.

Oral questions

Read each question twice. Allow about ten seconds after each reading.
1. Write the name of this shape (hold up a triangle).
2. How many sides does a square have?
3. What is this shape called (hold up a hexagon)?
4. How many sides does a pentagon have?
Note: Children will need a ruler to complete this sheet.

Common difficulties

It is important that children recognise shapes in different orientations (an 'upside down' triangle is still a triangle). Children should also be used to dealing with irregular as well as regular shapes (i.e. any shape with six straight sides is a hexagon). You may wish to point out that a square is a special type of rectangle, though other quadrilaterals (e.g. rhombus, parallelogram) should be avoided at this stage.

Practice activities

1 Place a selection of card shapes in a feely bag. Feel a shape, and guess its name – take it out to check.

2 Use a selection of card shapes. Draw round each one and name it. Inside, write its number of sides and corners.

Answers

1. triangle **2.** 4 **3.** hexagon **4.** 5

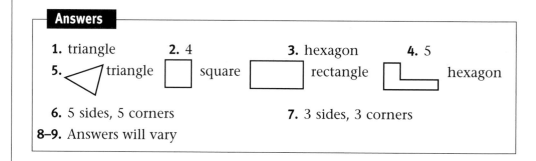
5. triangle   square   rectangle   hexagon

6. 5 sides, 5 corners   **7.** 3 sides, 3 corners
8–9. Answers will vary

Name _____

I. [ ]   2. [ ]   3. [ ]   4. [ ]

$\frac{\square}{4}$

5. Join each shape to the correct name.

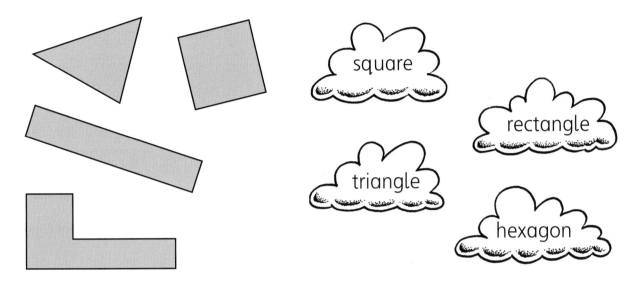

square

rectangle

triangle

hexagon

$\frac{\square}{4}$

Write how many sides and corners.

6. 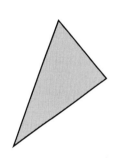   [ ] sides
            [ ] corners

7.   [ ] sides
         [ ] corners

$\frac{\square}{4}$

Use a ruler. Draw shapes to match.

8. 6 sides   **9.** 4 corners

$\frac{\square}{4}$

Score: [ ] /16   Total: [ ]

Line symmetry

Skills summary

- To recognise patterns that have line symmetry
- To recognise shapes that have line symmetry
- To locate a line of symmetry on a pattern or shape
- To create a symmetrical pattern or shape by folding and/or cutting paper
- To complete a symmetrical drawing given a line of symmetry and half the picture

Diagnostic materials

Shape, Space and Measures Workbook, page 33
- Check that the children can recognise symmetrical shapes.

Oral questions

Read each question twice. Allow about ten seconds after each reading.
Draw four shapes on the board:
1. A square
2. An equilateral triangle
3. A non-symmetrical hexagon
4. A non-symmetrical pentagon
Ask the children in turn whether or not each shape is symmetrical. They write yes or no.
Note: Children will need a ruler to complete this sheet.

Common difficulties

Children who have difficulty with line symmetry should be given plenty of opportunities to cut out and test shapes by folding. Emphasise that a shape is symmetrical if one side fits exactly over the other when it is folded. Some shapes can be folded in different ways and still match.
When children are completing a shape or pattern about a given line of symmetry, a mirror might be helpful.

Practice activities

1 Fold a piece of paper in two. How many different symmetrical shapes can you make with two straight cuts? Do any of them have other lines of symmetry? Repeat for three straight cuts.

2 Play with a partner. Use large-squared paper and counters. Draw a line on the paper. Place five counters on one side. Your partner must place five counters on the opposite side to make a symmetrical pattern. Play again, reversing roles.

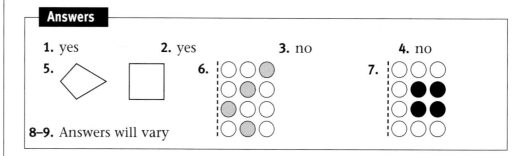

Answers

1. yes   **2.** yes   **3.** no   **4.** no
5.
8–9. Answers will vary

Name _____

I. 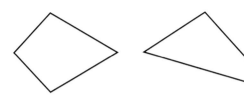 **2.**   **3.** 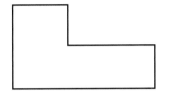 **4.**

$\frac{\quad}{4}$

5. Circle the shapes that have symmetry.

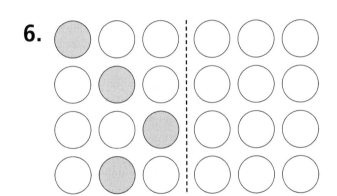

$\frac{\quad}{2}$

Colour circles on the right to make patterns with symmetry.

6.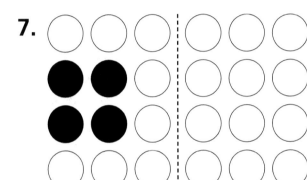

7.

$\frac{\quad}{4}$

Use a ruler. Draw two shapes that have symmetry.
Draw the lines of symmetry.

8.

9.

$\frac{\quad}{4}$

Score: [   ] /14   Total: [   ]

Sorting

Skills summary

- To construct and interpret a Venn diagram (two distinct criteria)
- To construct and interpret a Venn diagram (two non-distinct criteria)
- To sort a set of objects using a Venn diagram (two non-distinct criteria)
- To sort a set of numbers using a Venn diagram (two non-distinct criteria)

Diagnostic materials

Shape, Space and Measures Workbook, page 34
- Check that the children can sort accurately using a Venn diagram.

Oral questions

Read each question twice. Allow about ten seconds after each reading.
1. Which of these is more than 10? (Write 8, 5, 12 on the board.)
2. Which of these is less than 20? (Write 21, 6, 34 on the board.)
3. Which of these is odd and more than 10? (Write 9, 11, 4 on the board.)
4. Which of these is even and less than 12? (Write 12, 7, 8 on the board.)

Common difficulties

Children may have difficulties with sorting by two non-distinct criteria (e.g. even, more than 4). Emphasise that some numbers or objects can match more than one criteria. These need to be placed in the overlapping part of the diagram. Children will need to be systematic dealing with each number or object in turn, and deciding where on the diagram it should be placed. Sorting opportunities will often arise in other subject areas (e.g. science – floats/sinks, magnetic/not magnetic).
When sorting numbers children need to be clear about the vocabulary involved, and will need to be familiar with the number line. Practise activities using the line (e.g. point to a number more than 5 – note, 5 itself is not included).

Practice activities

1 Sort number cards (1 to 20) according to two distinct criteria (use a large Venn diagram). For example: (odd, even), (more than 8, less than 5). Repeat for non-distinct criteria, e.g. (more than 9, even). Where are the numbers that match neither criterion?

2 One child (or the teacher) sorts the number cards (1 to 20) according to two non-distinct criteria. Can the other child guess the criteria used?

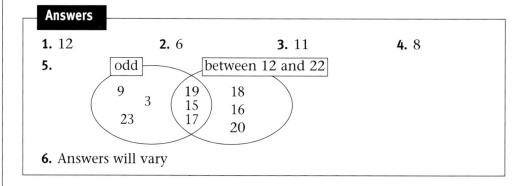

Answers

1. 12   **2.** 6   **3.** 11   **4.** 8

5.

odd: 9, 3, 23
between 12 and 22: 18, 16, 20
overlap: 19, 15, 17

6. Answers will vary

1. [ ]   **2.** [ ]   **3.** [ ]   **4.** [ ]

5. Write these numbers in the correct parts of the diagram.

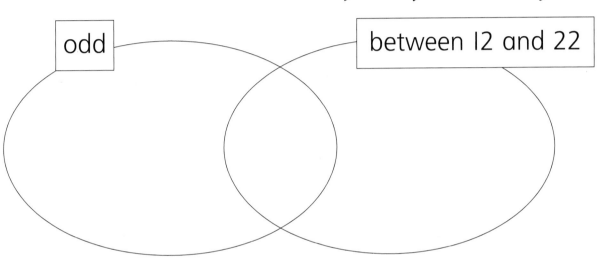

odd   between 12 and 22

6. Write two numbers in each part.

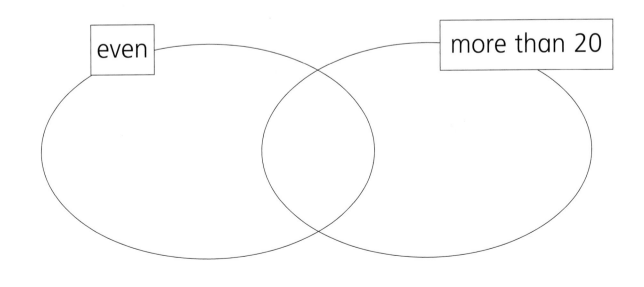

even   more than 20

Score: [ ] /16   Total: [ ]

Data

Skills summary

- To construct and interpret a Carroll diagram (two non-distinct criteria)
- To sort a set of objects using a Carroll diagram (two non-distinct criteria)
- To sort a set of numbers using a Carroll diagram (two non-distinct criteria)
- To collect data
- To construct and interpret a block graph
- To construct and interpret simple tables
- To sort data by listing it in a table

Diagnostic materials

Shape, Space and Measures Workbook, page 35
- Check that the children understand the Carroll diagram and can work systematically to complete it.

Shape, Space and Measures Workbook, page 37
- Check children can accurately complete a block graph.

Oral questions

Read each question twice. Allow about ten seconds after each reading.
1. Which of these is more than 20: 12, 28, 19?
2. Which of these is between 20 and 30: 56, 19, 27?
3. Which of these is odd and less than 10: 15, 18, 9, 4?
4. Which of these is even and more than 10: 8, 4, 18, 13?

Common difficulties

Children may find sorting onto a Carroll diagram difficult, because each object must be matched against two criteria before it can be entered. Provide plenty of practice, and encourage the children to be systematic. Children will enjoy using information that can change over time (e.g. age), so that the data has to be re-sorted. Constructing a block graph should not pose too many difficulties (ensure children know to add appropriate labels and titles). Children should be encouraged to use the block graph to extract information (e.g. How many more children liked strawberry ice-cream? What sort of person might find this information useful?).

Practice activities

1. Construct a class Carroll diagram that can be referred to each day (e.g. sort days of the week using: odd number of letters, even number of letters, has an 'e', does not have an 'e').

2. Conduct a survey on favourite sports (e.g. football, rugby, swimming, rounders). Construct a block graph to show how many children like each sport (label the axes and give it a title). Write some questions for someone else to answer, using the graph.

Answers

		1. 28	2. 27	3. 9	4. 18

5.		odd	even	6. 3	7. 5
less than 20		97	14 16	8. 8	9. 5
more than 20		27 23 31	22		

Name _____

1. ☐ **2.** ☐ **3.** ☐ **4.** ☐

☐
8

5. Write these numbers in the correct part of the diagram.

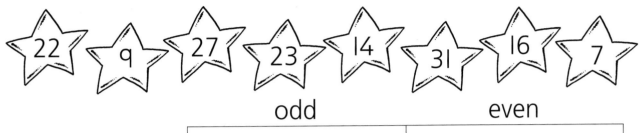

	odd	even
less than 20		
more than 20		

☐
4

How many children liked:

6. grapes? ☐

7. apples? ☐

8. oranges or bananas? ☐

9. grapes or oranges? ☐

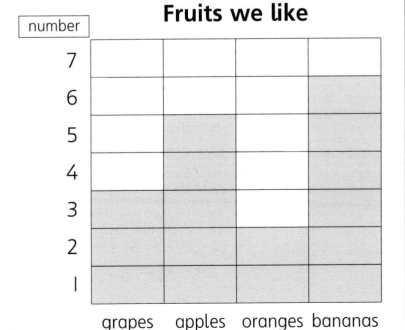

Fruits we like

☐
8

Score: ☐ /20   Total: ☐

Record keeping

The record keeping grid list the units (or groups of units) assessed in this book. Across the top is room for up to fifteen names. Within each box on the grid is space to record the score each pupil achieved, so that over the course of the year you can easily track progress.

Names															
N1, N2															
N3, N6															
N4															
N5															
N7, N8, N9															
N10, N11															
N12, N13															
N14															
N15, N16															
N17, N18															
N19															
N20															
N21, N22															
N23, N24															
N25															
N26															
N27															
N28, N29															
N30, N31															
N32															
N33															
N34, N36															
N35, N38															
N37															
N39, N40															
N41															
M1, M2															
M3, M4, M7															
M5															
M6, M8															
M9, M10, M11															
S1															
S3, S4															
S6															
D1, D4															
D3, D3, D5															